Disney's Year Book 1986

Disney's Year Book

1986

GROLIER ENTERPRISES INC.
Danbury, Connecticut

GROLIER ENTERPRISES INC.
Robert B. Clarke   *Publisher*

ISBN: 0-7172-8183-3
ISSN: 0273-1274

Illustration Credits and Acknowledgments

6—© 1984 Children's Television Workshop. Used by permission of
Children's Television Workshop; 7—Photo courtesy of Heath Co., Benton
Harbor, MI; 8—Photo courtesy of Axlon Co.; 9—Photo courtesy of
OWI Inc., Compton, CA; 10—left, Photo courtesy of Androbot, Inc., San
Jose, CA, right, Photo courtesy of TOMY Corp., Carson, CA; 11—Photo
courtesy of RB Robot Corp., Golden, CO; 24—Bud Symes © 1984;
25—© Tracy Frankel; 26—© Duomo/Dan Helms; 28—Bud Symes
© 1984; 29—left, © Duomo/David Madison, right, Bud Symes © 1984;
30-31—Jenny Tesar; 44—© Peter Arnold, Inc.; 46-47—© 1977 Walt
Disney Productions; 52—© Randa Bishop 1980; 53—Randa Bishop/
Black Star; 54—© Randa Bishop 1980; 55—© DPI/Randa Bishop;
68—© Nicholas Conte/Bruce Coleman, Inc.; 69—© Leonard Lee Rue
III/Animals Animals; 70—© Tom McHugh/Photo Researchers, Inc.;
71—© E.R. Degginger/Bruce Coleman, Inc.; 72—© Anthony Bannister/
Animals Animals; 73—Mike Neumann/Photo Researchers, Inc.; 74-75—
Reproduced by permission of Green Tiger Press, La Jolla, CA, 92038,
from the Book *Hanimals*, conceived by Mario Mariotti, with color
photographs by Roberto Marchiori. Copyright © 1980 by La Nuova
Italia Editrice S.p.A., Florence, Italy; 76—J.P. Laffont/Sygma; 77—
© Jacques Lamontagne; 78—© Ken Clark; 79—© Jacques Lamontagne;
80-83—Courtesy of Scholastic Photography Awards, conducted by
Scholastic Magazines, Inc. and sponsored by Eastman Kodak Company.

Contents

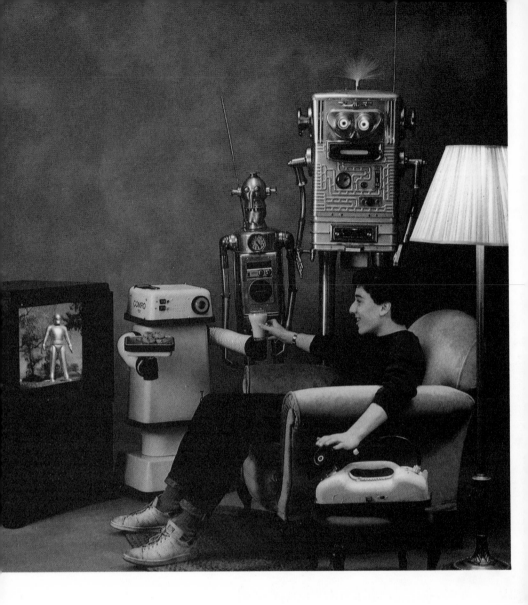

"Good Morning,
I Am Your Robot."

Meet Hubot, a streamlined, white box with two "eyes" and a friendly voice.

Hubot is efficient and hard working. If you tell it what to do, it will make your life a lot easier. Hubot can move and speak. It can wake you up, serve a meal, turn appliances on and off, and vacuum the rug. It can entertain you with its TV, radio, tapedeck, clock, and video game system. And no matter how many times you tell it to do something, it will never say "no" and never get tired.

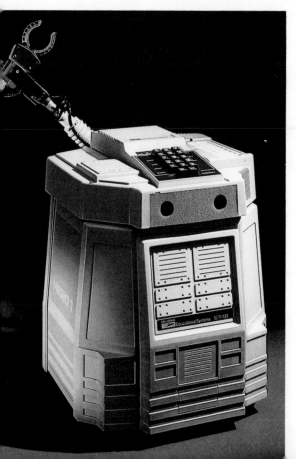

Home robots come in many different models (far left). The most popular is Hero (left). It has an arm that extends and a hand that can grip objects.

This robot cat purrs when you pet it.

Hubot is an amazing automatic machine— more commonly known as a robot—and before too long, a machine like Hubot may come to stay at your house.

Many home (or personal) robots look something like people. They have a headlike part with two "eyes." These "eyes" are actually electronic devices called sensors that register changes in light. The sensors tell the robot when something is in its way and the robot is then able to move around it.

The robot may also have an arm, or arms, attached to the sides of its body, and it may even have legs, although most home robots move around on wheels. Some robots also have artificial voices, but they can only speak a few words.

The earliest automatic machines could only do one thing. Today's robots have computer "brains," so they can be programmed to do a variety of things.

Most robots are designed to do things around the house. As they move, the robots travel along a path set by their computer. Hubot goes into action when you push a button or give it a verbal command. You can

Movit, a toy robot, has a built-in computer.

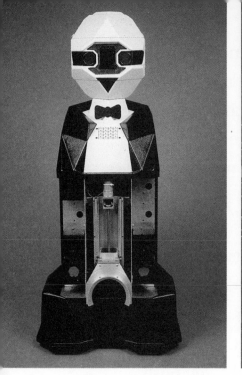 

B.O.B. (for Brains on Board*) speaks (left). Omnibot (right) wakes you in the morning.*

put cookies and milk on its serving tray (it has no arms) and send it from the kitchen to the living room. It will greet a person by saying, "Hello, it's good to see you. Please help yourself to cookies and milk."

Some robots can be used as security guards. Hero Jr., for example, can be programmed to stand in front of a window or a door, or to roam around the house. When its light sensors detect any movement, it says, "Intruder alert! Intruder alert! You have five seconds to signal the proper password." If the person gives the correct password, the robot says, "You may pass, friend." If no password is given, the robot sets off a loud alarm.

Robots may also be entertainment machines (like Hubot), or educational devices that teach people how robots work. Battery powered robot toys and "pets" have also become popular.

Scientists are working on ways to make home robots even more useful and amazing machines. Someday they may even be able to do homework!

RB5X sings, and plays "Spin the Robot."

minnie's MAKEOVER

"I want to try out for cheerleader this year," Minnie Mouse said to her friend Clarabelle. "Maybe that'll make Mickey notice me."

"Tryouts are in two weeks," Clarabelle pointed out. "Are you in shape?"

Minnie looked down at her thin legs and round bottom. "I'll get in shape," she said.

"You have to be pretty, and popular, too."

Minnie was sure she could make the cheering squad. She just had to make an effort.

Clarabelle wished Minnie luck, but she
wasn't sure Minnie could make herself over in
just two weeks.

That afternoon, Minnie joined an exercise
class. Then she bought a book on beauty and
some creams and makeup. And finally, she
got a book from the library on how to be
popular.

Every day, Minnie worked hard to get in
shape. She kicked her legs high. She
stretched to reach her toes. She ran in place
as hard as she could.

The other girls in the exercise class were
already in shape. They didn't huff and puff.
But Minnie hadn't been exercising. She *did*
huff and puff.

Getting in shape was harder than Minnie
had thought.

"Take it easy, Minnie," said Clarabelle.

"I can't," answered her friend. "I only have two weeks."

The next Saturday Clarabelle stopped by Minnie's house. When she saw what her friend was doing, she gasped.

Minnie was soaking her elbows in lemons to make them smooth. She had cucumber slices on her eyes so they wouldn't be puffy.

"After this, I'm going to wash my face in milk," she told her friend.

"All that food is making me hungry," said Clarabelle. "I'm going to make myself a sandwich. Would you like one?"

"Oh, no," answered Minnie. "I'm on a diet. But I can have half a cup of skim milk."

Clarabelle hoped Minnie was going to make the cheering squad. She was trying so hard.

The next time Clarabelle saw Minnie, she was about to practice what she had learned from the book on how to be popular.

"It says that when you meet someone, you should give him a big smile. Here comes Mickey. I'll try it out on him."

Minnie smiled her biggest smile. "Hello, Mickey," she said.

Mickey was puzzled. Why was Minnie smiling that funny-looking smile? Then he thought he understood.

"Just got your teeth cleaned, eh, Minnie? They look great. Hi, Clarabelle." And Mickey walked on toward the football field.

On the morning of the cheerleader tryouts, Minnie felt in shape, pretty and popular. She was ready to make the team.

At the tryouts, Minnie drew number five.
She would be the fifth one to try out.

The first girl got up. She picked up her
pompoms and took a last look at a piece of
paper she had been studying. Then she went
into her routine and performed it perfectly.

The second girl got up. She had also been

studying a piece of paper. Minnie wondered
what was on it, so she picked it up.

On the paper were three cheers, and
pictures of the movements that went with
them.

All of a sudden, Minnie was worried. She
had done a lot to prepare for this tryout. But

she hadn't learned any movements to go with the cheers.

When her number was called, Minnie did the best she could. She yelled the cheers, and waved her pompoms. She kicked up and jumped high in the air.

"Thank you, Minnie," said the coach. "I want you to wait here until the tryouts are over. I have something to say to you."

Poor Minnie! She thought the coach was going to scold her for not being prepared.

After the last girl had gone through her

routine, the coach went over to Minnie. "I guess you know you didn't make the squad," she said gently.

Minnie hung her head.

"But there's another job we need to fill. I think you'd be perfect for it."

Minnie sat up. She wasn't going to get a scolding, after all.

"We need a boy and a girl to play the Tiger Cub mascots," explained the coach. "You're just the right size for the mascot costume. Would you like the job?"

"Would I?" cried Minnie. "You bet!"

"You'll have to spend a lot of time practicing with the boy who plays the other part," said the coach.

"That's okay," said Minnie. "Who is he?"

"Here he comes now," answered the coach.

"Hi, Minnie," called Mickey. "Welcome to the Tiger Cubs!"

THE TRIATHLON:
FOR SUPER ATHLETES ONLY

You begin by swimming 2.4 miles in the ocean, kicking through strong tides and rolling waves.

Then you put on shoes, shorts, and a T-shirt, and climb on your bicycle. You pedal uphill and down for 112 miles.

Children starting a triathlon run (left).

And then you hop off your bike, drink some water, do a few exercises, and set out to run a marathon—a distance of 26 miles and 385 yards.

When, and if, you finish the marathon, you will have swum, biked, and run a distance of 140.6 miles—and it may have taken you 10 or 15 hours to do it!

In children's triathlons, cyclists wear hard helmets for safety.

Triathlon swimmers often have to battle high waves in rough ocean waters.

This amazing athletic contest is called a triathlon (because it involves three sports). Triathlons began in 1978 on the island of Oahu, Hawaii. Only 14 men took part in the first Hawaiian triathlon, called the Ironman Championship. But each year, the Hawaiian triathlon has become more and more popular.

In 1985, 1,250 men and women competed in the Ironman Championship. And triathlons are now held all over the United States and in foreign countries, too.

Most of these triathlons are shorter than the 140.6 miles of the Hawaiian one. But they still require amazing strength and endurance.

Championship athletes like Dave Scott who take part in triathlons must truly be in super condition. Dave Scott has won the Hawaiian Ironman Championship four times. In 1984 he set a record by completing the course in eight hours, 54 minutes, and 20 seconds.

To become a winner, Dave Scott trained very hard. He started every day at 6:30 in the morning. First he ran 10 or 15 miles. Then he biked 75 miles. Then he lifted weights. And to cool off after that, he swam three miles.

He was also on a special vegetarian diet. He ate 15 pieces of fruit a day, four or five huge salads, and large amounts of rice, yogurt, and low-fat cottage cheese.

Triathlons have now become a sport for children as well as adults. In 1985, one program called IronKids held triathlons for

Young biker looks happy after finishing (left).
Runner (right) carries her own water bottle.

boys and girls aged seven to 14 in a number
of American cities.

The winners of these triathlons then
competed in a championship held in October
at DisneyWorld in Orlando, Florida.

The distances that children swim, bike, and
run are much shorter than those in adult
triathlons. For example, IronKids aged seven
to 10 swim 100 meters (109.3 yards), bike five

Swimmer prepares for race (left). Winners of a California triathlon display their prizes (right).

kilometers (3.12 miles), and run one kilometer (⅝ of a mile). For IronKids aged 11 to 14, these distances are doubled.

The organizers of children's triathlons make sure that the kids entering them are healthy and that the course is simple and safe. The triathlons encourage children to learn new skills, to improve their physical condition, and above all, to have fun.

Super Sweats

Super athletes like the ones who compete in triathlons deserve super sweat shirts. You can decorate your sweat shirt with one of the designs shown here, with your name, or with a football, baseball, or tennis racket for your favorite sport.

What You Need
Sweat shirt, felt, scissors, towel, pencil.

What To Do

1. Wash the felt so it doesn't shrink when you wash the sweat shirt. Press the water out of the felt with a towel—don't wring it out or it will wrinkle. Lay the felt on a flat surface until it's dry.

2. Trace a design on the felt, like the hearts or hands shown here. Use as many colors of felt as you like. Cut out the design.

3. Sew the pieces of felt on your sweat shirt.

GLASS REUNION

"Three years!" Doc said. "My, how flime ties!"

"You mean 'time flies,' " Grumpy snorted.

"That's what I said," Doc replied.

"Shoosh, you two!" said Happy. "We've got to *think!*"

What the Seven Dwarfs had to think about was an anniversary present for Snow White and her Prince. In just two days, it would be their third wedding anniversary. The Seven

Dwarfs still hadn't thought of a gift for the happy pair.

The Dwarfs went back to work in their diamond mine. Each of them was thinking about what to give Snow White and the Prince. Dopey grabbed a diamond from the diamond car.

"Dopey says we can give her diamonds," Sneezy translated.

Doc shook his head. "No, Dopey! For third wedding anniversaries, you're supposed to give a gift made of *glass*."

"That's silly," Grumpy grumped.

"That's the rule," Doc said, swinging his pickaxe. Then he struck the wall of the mine, and the wall began to crumble!

"Look!" cried Happy. "It's a *tunnel!*" Doc had uncovered a hidden tunnel in the wall of the diamond mine!

The Seven Dwarfs peeked cautiously into the tunnel. "Looks spooky," Bashful said.

"W-we ought to explore it," said Doc.

So the seven little men entered the dark, damp tunnel. Their lanterns cast long, spidery shadows against the walls.

"Keep close together, men!" Doc whispered. "There are other tunnels going off in all directions! It'd be mighty easy to get lost in here!"

At last the tunnel came to an end at a tall wooden door.

"It's probably locked!" Grumpy said. "No sense trying it!"

Doc pressed the door latch. The door creaked open!

The flickering light from the seven lanterns revealed a big, dungeon-like chamber, with cobwebs hanging everywhere. In the center of the room was a table. On it were strange jars filled with colored liquids and powders. On the floor was a broken goblet. Dust covered everything.

"What *is* this place?" said Happy.

No one answered because no one knew. Only Snow White's wicked stepmother had ever known about this room. For this was

where the evil Queen had kept her books of spells, her secret potions, and her Magic Mirror!

And there it was, three years later, on the wall where the Queen had left it!

"Perfect!" Doc exclaimed, when he saw the
beautiful mirror. "I think we've just found
Snow White's anniversary present!"

Two days later, the Seven Dwarfs
presented Snow White and the Prince with
the mirror. It was all shiny and sparkling like
new.

"It's beautiful!" Snow White exclaimed.
She gave each of her seven little friends a
kiss on each of their seven little foreheads.

Immediately, she told the Royal Carpenter

to hang the mirror over her dressing table.

That evening, Snow White began to comb her hair, gazing at herself in the mirror. Then she put down her brush. "Now, then," she said, "where did I put my hairpins?"

She didn't notice what was happening to her mirror. Snow White's reflection had vanished. In its place was a ghostly face.

And then it spoke!

"Snow White, Snow White, search no more! Your pins are in the second drawer!"

Well, you could have knocked Snow White over with a feather! "Who-who said that?" she managed to say.

The mirror answered her question.

"Infinitely wise am I,
  Knowing all of earth and sky.
Or, to put it somewhat clearer,
  'Twas I who spoke—your Magic
    Mirror!"

"My word!" said the Prince when Snow White told him about the mirror. "I'm sure the Seven Dwarfs don't know this is the Magic Mirror. We must return it to them."

The next morning, Snow White and the Prince put the Magic Mirror in the royal coach and drove to the Dwarfs' diamond mine.

Six of the Seven Dwarfs ran out to meet

them. "Thank heaven you've come!" said Doc.

"Dopey's lost in the tunnel!" Sneezy added quickly.

"The silly fool went back for his lantern all alone," Grumpy said. "He left it where we found the mirror!"

Dopey had wandered off into one of the many side tunnels that led away from the main tunnel. Since he couldn't yell for help, they couldn't find him.

The Prince said he would go get his
soldiers to look for Dopey.

But Snow White had another idea. "Let's
ask the Magic Mirror!"

Magic Mirror? The Dwarfs looked at each
other. What did Snow White mean?

The Prince took the mirror out of the
coach.

"Where is Dopey, Magic Mirror?" Snow
White pleaded.

Once again, the ghostly face appeared.

"To find your wandering friend, Snow White,

Look in the third tunnel on the right!"

Once Dopey had been found, they all decided that Snow White and the Prince should keep the mirror. And, to thank the Magic Mirror for rescuing him, Dopey made a promise. He would come over to Snow White's castle every Saturday morning to polish it.

TICKLE TICKLE, GIGGLE GIGGLE

You know that you feel good when you laugh. But did you know that laughter can actually make you a happier and healthier person? That's what some scientists have concluded after studying how and why people laugh.

Humans are the only animals that have the ability to laugh at whatever they think is funny. Chimpanzees and some other apes can laugh, but only when they're tickled.

Human babies start to laugh when they're about ten weeks old. By the time they're four months old, they're laughing about once an hour. And four-year-old children laugh as often as every four minutes.

The average adult laughs fifteen times a day, with each laugh lasting anywhere from half a second to a minute. An especially cheery person may laugh as many as 400 times during a day. And laughter is contagious. If one person cracks up, others are likely to do the same.

Everyone's laugh is different. A person's chest capacity and vocal power help determine what kind of laugh he or she has.

When you see or hear something funny, your brain sends signals along nerves

throughout your body. The signals tell your glands to produce body chemicals. These chemicals make you more alert, and they make your heart and lungs work faster. The muscles of your throat, chest, and stomach tighten up and this makes air build up in your lungs. You let loose with a roar of laughter when your stomach and chest muscles suddenly force the air out of your lungs past your vocal chords. The air may rush out of your lungs as fast as 70 miles an hour!

After you stop laughing, your muscles are more relaxed. And you are less likely to think about things that have been upsetting you.

Laughter seems to help all kinds of medical problems—from headaches and infections to arthritis. Laughter can also help people forget they are in pain.

Hospitals now use comedy skits, funny books, records and movies to help people feel better and recover faster from medical problems. Doctors and nurses find that when people laugh they feel less depressed and less frightened about their illnesses.

Laughter will never replace medical science, of course. And it won't cure a cold. But a good laugh can make you feel better, happier and healthier. No kidding!

Have You Heard This One?

What did one eye say to the other eye?
Just between you and me, something
smells.

BABY CELERY: "Mama, where did I
come from?"
MOTHER CELERY: "Hush, dear. The
stalk brought you."

BILL: "Is it bad luck to have a cat follow
you?"
PHIL: "It depends. Are you a man or a
mouse?"

Why do bumblebees hum?
They know the tune but not the words.

MOTHER: "Mary, if you eat the rest of that cake, you'll burst."
MARY: "Okay. Pass the cake and duck!"

FATHER: "At your age I could name all the presidents—and in proper order, too."
SON: "Yes, but then there were only three or four of them."

MOTHER: "Now Elizabeth, don't you know you aren't supposed to eat peas with your knife?"

ELIZABETH: "I know, Mom, but my fork leaks."

How can you make a baby buggy?
Tickle the baby's toes.

Why does an Indian chief wear so many feathers?
To keep his wigwam.

Why does the Statue of Liberty stand in New York Harbor?
Because it can't sit down.

Why are dentists such sad people?
Because they are always looking down in the mouth.

Which member of a baseball team wears the largest hat?
The one with the largest head.

Why did Adam take a bite out of the apple?
He didn't have a knife or fork.

What is full of holes, yet can hold water?
A sponge.

CLOWNING AROUND

Clowns are funny. They tumble into the circus arena and keep the audience laughing while other acts are going on. For many people, clowns are the best part of the circus.

What does it take to be a clown? A lot more than a funny suit and some makeup. A clown may spend years developing a special character and appearance. A clown must also be able to perform dozens of gags and be skilled in juggling, unicycle riding, stilt walking, and acrobatics.

Where do circuses find people with these talents? The Ringling Brothers and Barnum & Bailey Circus trains its clowns. In 1968 the

Student clowns at Clown College spend hours learning to put on makeup (left and below).

circus opened Clown College in Venice, Florida.

Each year 4,000 to 5,000 hopeful clowns apply. Only 60 are accepted. Of these, fewer than 20 will be offered contracts by the circus after they've been trained.

The Clown College course lasts about two months. The students attend classes in acrobatics and the other skills they'll need as professionals, and they practice their stunts and gags until late at night. At the end of the course, the clowns perform for the circus producers, who choose the new clowns.

A clown's costume may cost $2,000.

No two clowns dress or look exactly alike. All have different costumes and makeup.

The student clowns work on their costumes, makeup, and on developing a character. They may be jokers who throw pies. They may be silly, clumsy clowns who can't do anything right. Or they may be a special character, such as a policeman.

After they graduate from Clown College, the new clowns will continue to develop their skills. And they will get better and better at their job—clowning around to make you laugh.

THE COLD GIANT

Once upon a time, there was a tiny village
where folks were very friendly.

On a hill above the village was a big castle.
But no one ever visited it.

One day a little boy named Ivan asked his
mother about the castle. She told him that

the cold giant once lived there. And in those days the village was a cold, unfriendly place.

"It's not like that now," said Ivan.

"That's because the cold giant went away," replied his mother. "Now it's always warm and sunny, and people are friendly."

"What did the cold giant look like, Mother?" asked Ivan.

"No one knows," answered his mother. "We never saw him. We knew he was there because it was so cold. But no one ever visited him. I guess we were afraid."

The next morning when Ivan woke up, he saw a strange thing. There was snow on the ground!

"Mother!" cried Ivan, running into the kitchen. "Is the cold giant back?"

"He must be," said his mother, shivering even though she wore her warmest robe.

Ivan's family ate breakfast in silence.
Everyone was very cold. No one even wanted
to talk.

The snow was so deep and the day was so
cold, that Ivan couldn't go outside to play.
For several days, it was the same—all the
people stayed inside their houses. And
everyone got very grouchy.

Ivan was tired of sitting in the house. He
was tired of doing nothing. And he was tired
of being grouchy. So he decided to do
something. He decided to visit the cold giant
in the big cold castle on the hill.

Late that night, when everyone was asleep, Ivan put on three pairs of socks, two pairs of mittens, a sweater, a muffler and a hat. Then he set out for the castle.

When Ivan got to the castle, he found the big front door standing open. Snow was blowing into the hall. As Ivan went in, the icy floor crunched under his boots.

On the first floor, Ivan found a big room with a huge fireplace. It looked as if it hadn't seen a fire in many years. He also found a stairway, so he went upstairs.

On the second floor of the castle was a long hallway that led to a bedroom. Very carefully, Ivan opened the bedroom door.

There, lying on the stone floor and snoring, was the cold giant. He shivered as he snored.

Ivan felt sorry for the giant, but he was afraid to awaken him. Then he had an idea.

Hurrying out of the castle and down the hill, Ivan went to his family's woodpile. He picked up as much wood as he could carry, and hurried back up the hill to the cold giant's castle.

Ivan built a big fire in the castle's fireplace. Then, as the room began to get warm, Ivan's eyes began to close. There was a sofa in front of the fireplace, so he lay down on it and fell asleep.

Upstairs, the giant was waking up. He stretched and looked around. Something was happening. Why, he was warm! The giant got up and went downstairs. He saw the fire in the fireplace.

"Oh, goody!" said the giant. He plopped himself down in front of the fire and stretched his feet out to feel the heat. He wiggled his toes and began to giggle.

The giant's giggles woke up Ivan. When he saw how happy the giant was, he began to giggle, too.

The giant leaped to his feet. "Who are you?" he asked.

"My name is Ivan," the little boy said. He reached up and gave the giant a hug. "I live in the village down below."

The giant hugged Ivan back. "How nice of you to visit me," he said. "No one ever does. And thank you for building me a fire. Would you like to stay and play with me?"

"I can't right now," said Ivan, for he saw that it was daylight. "I must go home, or my mother will worry. But I'll come back."

As Ivan waved goodbye to the giant, he
noticed something. The snow was melting,
and the day was nice and warm. In the
village below he saw his friends playing
outdoors.

"Mother!" he called when he saw her on the
front step. "I have a new friend!"

"That's nice, dear," she answered. "Why
don't you bring him home for dinner?"

"Gosh, Mom," said Ivan, "that's a great
idea!"

Ivan went running back up the hill to the
castle. "Mother says you can come for
dinner," he shouted to the giant.

The giant couldn't believe his ears. "Why,
no one ever invited me anywhere before," he

said. His eyes got very shiny, as if he were
going to cry.

That afternoon, Ivan rode home in the
giant's arms. When his mother saw him, she
was afraid. Then Ivan said, "Mother, this is
my new friend, the cold giant."

"New friend?" she said. "But we all
thought he had gone away. The weather isn't
cold any more."

"I built him a fire, and that made him nice
and warm," Ivan explained. "All it took was a
couple of logs."

But Ivan's mother knew better. "What it

took was a little boy and a big hug," she said.

And from that day on, the people in the village lived happily and warmly ever after. And so did the giant.

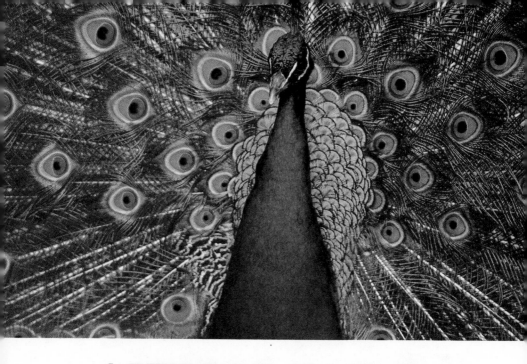

ANIMAL TAILS
A Long, Short, Straight, and Curly Story

Animals use their tails in many different ways. An animal may use its tail to help it run and jump, fly and swim, hunt and fight, scare off its enemies, flirt with the opposite sex, and show feelings like anger or fright.

Birds would have a hard time flying and most fish would be helpless in the water if they had no tails. Birds use their tails to help them steer and balance themselves in the air. Short-tailed birds like ducks have trouble steering when they are flying. That's why they almost never make quick turns in the air.

Fish use their tails like propellers as they swim. They twist their bodies and move their tail fins from side to side to move forward.

The male peacock (left) spreads its beautiful tail to attract a mate. The opossum (below) uses its curly tail to hold on to tree limbs.

Land animals use their tails to help them keep their balance as they run and jump. When a kangaroo makes a giant leap, its tail balances the weight of its body. If it had no tail, a kangaroo would topple over when it tried to jump.

Some animals, like alligators and crocodiles, use their tails when they hunt. Alligators and crocodiles lash out with their tails to knock down animals like deer or pigs

A sitting kangaroo supports itself with its tail.

A skunk lifts its tail before spraying its enemies.

that come to the water's edge. Then they attack the animals with their strong jaws.

The skunk uses its tail to scare off its enemies. Under its tail the skunk has glands that spray a terrible-smelling liquid for a distance of 10 to 15 feet. When a skunk is getting ready to spray this liquid, it turns its back and raises its tail. This is a signal for other animals (and people, too) to stay away!

Some birds use their tails to send a different kind of message. Male birds like

A porcupine's tail has many hooked quills.

peacocks often have large and colorful tail
feathers. When a peacock wants to attract
the attention of a female, he spreads his tail
feathers out behind him like a large fan. Then
he walks around proudly, turning slowly as
the female watches him.

Some animals have very dangerous tails. A
porcupine has 30,000 sharp quills hidden
under the long fur of its body. Many of these
quills are in its tail. During a fight, the
porcupine turns its back and slaps at its
enemy with its tail, sending hundreds of

needle-like quills into its enemy's body. The quills have hooks and they stay caught under the animal's skin.

Sometimes an animal's tail can send a message about the way the animal feels. A nervous squirrel will move its tail quickly from side to side. The more nervous the squirrel is, the faster its tail will flick.

When a cat is angry or frightened, its tail will swell to three times its normal size. (This happens because the tail fur stands on end.) When a dog is feeling playful, it will wag its tail slowly from side to side in wide sweeps. And when a dog is being scolded, it will hide its tail between its legs.

The stingray can hurt other sea creatures with its tail, which has sharp, poisonous spines.

Handy Dandy
HANIMALS

A giraffe wouldn't be a giraffe
without a long neck.

Why go to the zoo when you can create your own crew of striped and spotted creatures?

All it takes to make these handy Hanimals is some paint and a little imagination. Use nontoxic poster paints that will wash off easily when your zoo closes. Paint the animal's eyes right on your hand. Or make the eyes by painting buttons or Ping-Pong balls and gluing them to your hand with glue that washes off easily.

A zebra always shows its stripes.

And after you've done some Hanimals from the zoo, see if you can create your own dog or cat, or that pink piglet you saw on the farm last summer.

A dalmation is a dog with lots of spots.

Lighting Up the Sky

Few things are more exciting than the sight of fireworks exploding in the night sky.

Listen closely as you stare at the darkness above you. First you hear a distant popping sound. Then there's a long whistling *hisss*. Suddenly the fireworks go off! The sky lights

Brilliant fireworks displays light up the sky over New York City (left) and Montreal (below).

up and a fantastic shower of colored stars drifts slowly to earth.

Fireworks have been one of the most popular forms of entertainment for centuries. Probably they were invented about 900 years ago by the Chinese, who also invented gunpowder, which is used to make fireworks. Displays of fireworks soon became a popular way to celebrate great events such as the crowning of a king or queen.

In the United States, displays of fireworks have been a part of the celebration of

Modern science has made it possible to explode fireworks in many shapes, such as this palm tree (above) and beautiful flowers (right).

Independence Day—the Fourth of July—
almost since the founding of our country. For
many years, people celebrated the Fourth of
July by setting off firecrackers and other
fireworks in their back yards. Home
fireworks are now banned because they are
dangerous. But displays of fireworks in the
sky are more popular than ever. In 1976,
when America celebrated its bicentennial—
the 200th anniversary of its birth—there
were fireworks displays all over the United
States, and Americans cheered as shower
after shower of colored stars lit up the sky.

Building Bridges of Friendship *(left) by Robert Alaantara, Jr., South San Gabriel, California.* Here Comes the Sun *(above) by John B. Moore, Irving, Texas.* Peek-a-Boo *(right) by Rhonda Zimmer, West Frankfort, Illinois.*

WINDOW ON THE WORLD

How does a camera "take" a picture?
Basically, the camera is a box, with a window
on one side. The window is called a lens. The
lens lets light into the camera. When light
strikes the film, it forms a picture.

The photographer aims the camera's
window at the world—and takes pictures of
things wonderful to see.

Stoplight *by Paul LaGumina, Burbank, California.*

The photographs on these pages were among the winners in the 1985 Scholastic/Kodak Photo Award Program. This program is open to students in junior and senior high schools in the United States and Canada. The winners receive scholarships and other awards.

Fast Motion *(right)* by *James Minstrell, Bellevue, Washington.* Man Sitting on Park Bench *(below)* by *James Schmid, Charlotte, North Carolina.*

A PUPPY DOG TALE

"Pongo, where are you?" called Perdita.

"In here, Perdita," answered her mate.
"What is it?"

"Three of the puppies are missing!" she
told him.

"Are you sure?" Pongo replied. "Maybe
you miscounted."

But Perdita was not mistaken. Rolly and
Penny and Lucky were missing. "It's that
DeVil woman again, I know it," she said.

She was talking about Cruella DeVil, who
had stolen their puppies once before. Pongo
and Perdita had rescued and adopted the
puppies Cruella had collected to make herself
a fur coat. Now all 101 Dalmatians lived
happily together in Cruella's old house in the
country.

Pongo went out and started the Twilight
Bark. His message was passed from dog to
dog. Finally it reached a terrier in London

who lived near Cruella. When the terrier
went to spy on her, he found her fixing up her
house. But he didn't see any puppies.

The terrier sent a message back to Pongo:
"Woof, arf, woof! Woof, rowf! No Dalmatian
puppies here."

"Then where can they be?" asked Perdita.

"I don't know," answered Pongo. "They
must be somewhere. Let's ask the Colonel to
help us find them."

Pongo went to see
the big old sheepdog.

"Three puppies,
you say, old boy?"
said the Colonel.
"Let's consult Tibs."

Sergeant Tibs, the cat, thought they should form search parties as soon as the sun rose.

The next morning, Pongo, Perdita, and the remaining puppies got together with the Colonel and Sergeant Tibs. Then they began to search. They looked all over the neighborhood.

Not one puppy did they find!

Poor Perdita! She was so worried.

"There, there, Mrs. Pongo," said the cat. "Did you search inside the house?"

"Why, no," said Perdita. "I called for them, but I didn't look."

"They might be lost in that old house," said Tibs. "It's an odd place, you know. It has secret panels and hidden passages. We'd better look inside."

The search parties broke up again to look through the rambling old house. One by one they reported back to Sergeant Tibs: no puppies had been found. The only one who

didn't report back was Pongo.

They all waited for him. "Maybe he's found them," suggested the Colonel.

"Oh dear," wailed Perdita. "Now one more Dalmatian is missing."

The Colonel patted her dainty paw with his big fuzzy one. "There, there," he said. "You mustn't worry."

"But I *am* worried," she said. "And I'm not going to sit here and do nothing. Come on—we'll search again."

Perdita led the Colonel and Tibs and the puppies all through the house. They looked in closets. They looked under beds. They looked behind sofas. But they found no sign of Pongo or the missing puppies.

At last they came to a stairway. When they
got to the top, Perdita bumped into a wall.

"I guess we'll have to go back," she said.
As she turned around, she brushed against a
picture that was hanging on the wall.

Suddenly they all heard a creaking sound.
The wall was opening!

Sergeant Tibs quickly stepped in front of
Perdita. "Let me, Mrs. Pongo," he offered.
"It might be dangerous."

Tibs stood very straight, and fluffed his tail
out, so he would look bigger. Then he
carefully leaned into the dark opening. "Is
anyone in there?" he called.

They all waited in suspense. No one
answered. Tibs was about to call again, when

suddenly he was bowled over by something
black and white and wiggly. Tibs fell back
onto Perdita, and they all went tumbling
down the stairs.

Perdita picked herself
up. Then she saw
what had knocked
them down.

"Lucky! Penny!
Rolly! Where have
you been?" she cried.

"We were exploring . . ." said Lucky.
". . . and we found a secret passage . . ."
added Rolly.

". . . and we couldn't get out!" wailed
Penny.

"I found the same secret passage," said
Pongo. "I couldn't get out, either."

"Well, I guess it's a good thing we didn't
stop looking for you," said Perdita. "Come

on, let's see what Nanny has made for dinner.
I'll bet there's enough for Tibs and the
Colonel, too."

And they all trooped off to the kitchen for
one of Nanny's delicious doggy stews.